Livi

Heartlake Superstars!

CONTENTS

Girl Band

It's open-mic night, and the Heartlake City friends are about to go on stage! Use the clues to guess what each girl is doing in the band, and then write their names in the right boxes.

Stephanie

I hope none of the strings break during my solo.

Olivia

Did I remember to bring all the records?

Celebrity Style

Livi-mania has taken over Heartlake City, and everyone wants to look like the famous singer! Use your pinkest pen to colour the girls' hair and give them all a Livi makeover.

4

Hair-mazing!

It's time for a real makeover at the hairdresser! The friends are running late and don't have time to chat – can you help them through the maze so they don't bump into anyone?

At the Salon

The friends made it to Natasha's salon just in time! Can you spot ten differences between the two pictures on the opposite page? Look carefully – the second picture is a mirror image, to make things extra tricky.

Stylish Hairdo

The magazines at Natasha's salon have all the latest hairstyles in them.
Number the covers in order of how much you like them, starting with your favourite!

Cute cut

Wild and wavy

Pretty ponytail

Short and sharp

Shutting Up Shop

Natasha is going to Livi's concert and she needs to close her salon at 4 p.m.
Draw circles round the appointments she will need to reschedule.

No Name

The girls are having a great time in their band, but they still don't have a name! Help them come up with a cool band name and write it in the space below.

Spinning Around

Uh-oh! DJ Olivia's discs are out of order. Look carefully at the pattern. Can you put the missing records back in the right order by writing the letters in the circles?

Special Guests

Lots of different people stay at the Heartlake Grand Hotel – today they have a singer, a painter, a couple and a family. Show the guests to their rooms by matching their numbers to the picture that suits them best.

Wish You Were Here!

The souvenir shop sells postcards of different parts of Heartlake City. Read the captions and then draw pictures for the ones that are blank.

In the jungle

City centre

In the mountains

At the beach

By the lake

Photo Fun

The girls love taking silly pictures together!
Read these top tips for fun poses to try with your friends.

- Try posing as your favourite animals – will you be a growling grizzly bear or a sweet bunny rabbit?

- Take a picture of just your hands! Looking at it later, can you remember which hand belongs to whom?

- Action shots look amazing! Time the picture to try to catch your friends jumping in the air – who jumped the highest?

Photo Fact!

Some people think that saying 'Cheese!' as your photo is taken gives you the perfect smile. Try it in the mirror – what do you think?

Can you spot which two of these selfies are identical?

Lost Luggage

It's time for Livi's tour . . . but these suitcases have lost their tags!
Look closely at the X-rays, then write the letters in the correct spaces
to match each bag with its proper owner.

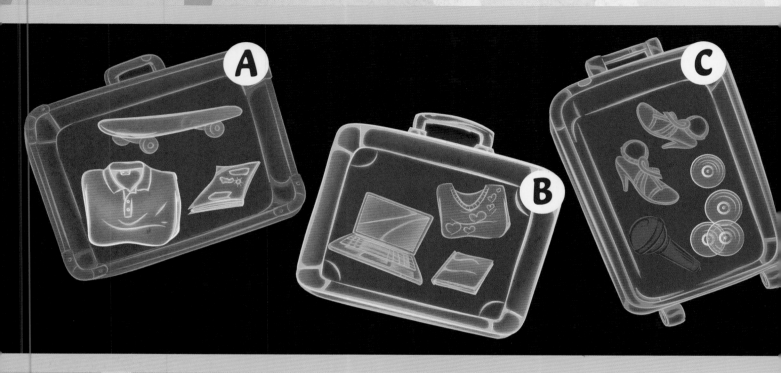

Hotel Mystery

Only a few people at the hotel know which room Livi is staying in. Look at the *sequence* of symbols on the tag below and use it to find your way to her room.

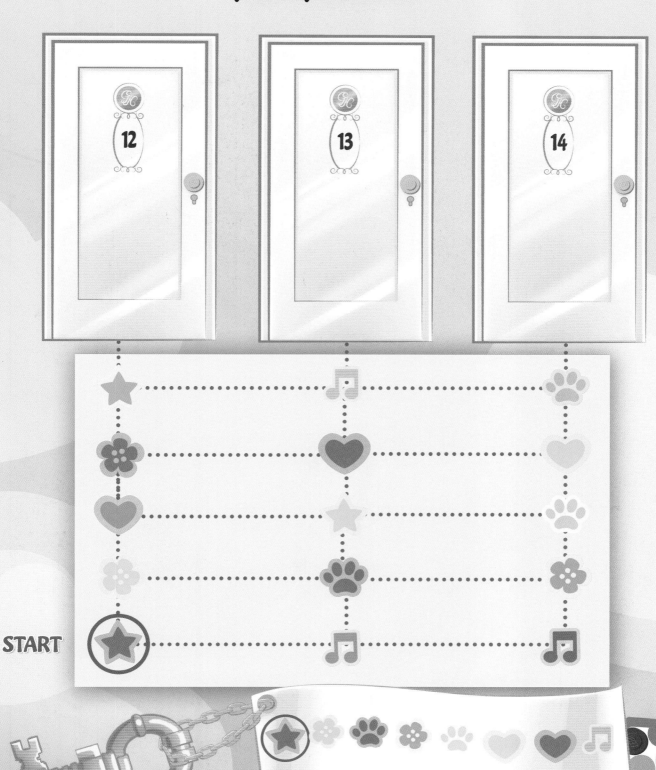

START

Poster Girl

Stephanie is working on a poster for Livi's concert. Which one is your favourite? Colour in the musical notes to rate each poster and help Stephanie choose the best one!

Now pretend that you're a pop star, too!
Design a poster for your own big performance.

Lots of Luggage!

Livi is known for taking lots of luggage on tour – but how much does it weigh?
Add up the numbers on the tags and circle the scales that show
the right weight below.

One of a Kind

Livi has lots of lovely shoes, but they've all got a bit mixed up!
Look carefully in her wardrobe. Can you spot the shoe that
doesn't have a pair?

Off to Work!

All the friends have cool after-school jobs! Can you help to complete the pictures? Choose the five correct squares from the opposite page and draw lines to where they belong.

Now write the correct number in the shape next to each girl to match them to their job.

1 Pizza-delivery person

2 Interior designer

3 Dog walker

4 IT instructor

5 Smoothie seller

Secret Talent

At the beach . . .

Look! There's Stephanie.

Shhh! Listen . . .

Wow! Stephanie totally . . .

. . . rocks!

This will make the best ringtone ever!

26

Bike Style

Emma is going to a sports shop to buy some cool accessories for her new bike.
Tick the items you think she should get.

Scent Sudoku

The girls stopped at the perfume shop and made quite a mess!
Help them put the bottles of perfume back on the shelves.
The same bottle must not be repeated in any row, column or 2x2 square.

A

B

C

D

Green Living

Mia always has loads of energy because she eats lots of fruit and veg!
Find these four sets of her favourite green snacks in the grid below.

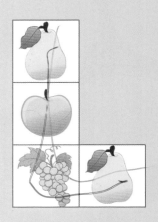  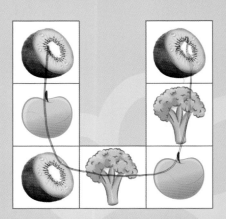 

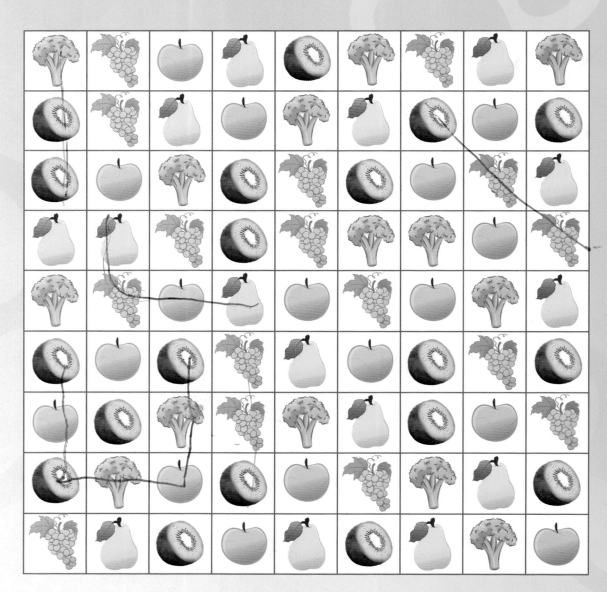

Perfect Pizza

The girls have shopped all morning and now it's time for pizza.
If they each want two slices, which plate has the right amount for everyone?

A

B

C

D

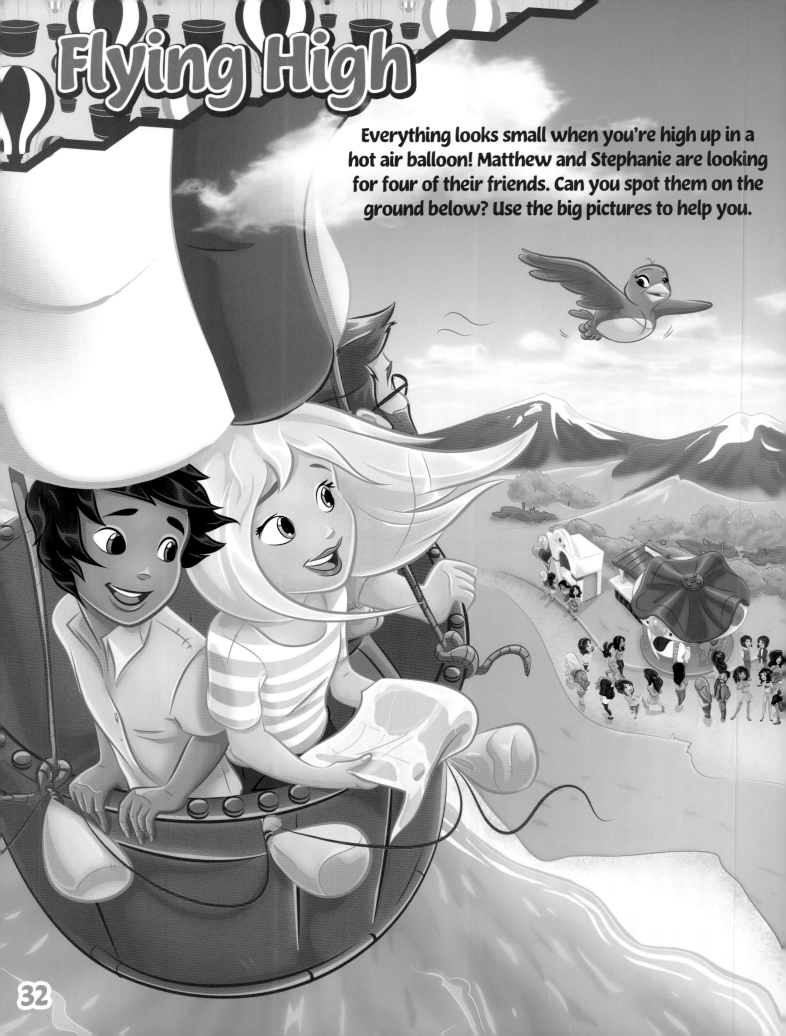

Flying High

Everything looks small when you're high up in a hot air balloon! Matthew and Stephanie are looking for four of their friends. Can you spot them on the ground below? Use the big pictures to help you.

Mystery Model

Who's the mystery model? Use the number key to colour in the picture and find out!

1  2 3 4 5 6

A Special Gift

The friends wanted to make Olivia a special pre[sent].
Look at the picture and find the gift decorated
with the most hearts. That's the best
present for Olivia!

Secret Messages

The Heartlake City girls love sending each other secret messages.
Follow these instructions to make your own!

You will need:

- two sheets of paper
- scissors
- a pencil
- coloured pens

1 Fold one sheet of paper in half and draw half a heart on it, as shown. Ask an adult to cut it out.

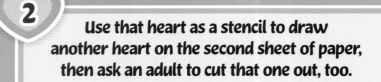

2 Use that heart as a stencil to draw another heart on the second sheet of paper, then ask an adult to cut that one out, too.

3 Put the two hearts together and write your secret message inside the heart.

Hi Mia . . .

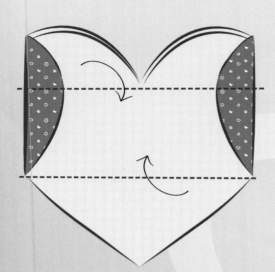

4 Fold the left and right sides over, as shown.

5 Turn the heart upside down. Look at where the dashed lines are on the diagram above and fold the top and bottom of the heart along those lines into the middle. It should look like an envelope.

Now give your note to a special friend!

Red Carpet

Oh no, a piece of Livi's VIP red carpet is missing! Choose the right piece to complete the carpet. The number of stars at each end should match the pieces they are touching.

B

C

A

D

All Set?

Stephanie is checking that things are ready for Livi's arrival. Take a look at the list below. Which two things aren't in the singer's dressing room yet?

Wish list:

- ✔️ Tulips
- ☐ Water
- ☐ Forest-fruit ice-cream dessert
- ☐ Exercise mat
- ☐ Bowl for doggie snacks
- ☐ Portrait of Livi's pet

Dance Steps

Step to the right

Step to the left

Step forward

Step backwards

Turn around

Jump

Livi has lots of dances to learn for her concert! Can you make up some more steps? Use the code to draw them in the space below, then try the moves yourself!

We Love Livi!

The concert was awesome! Fill in the speech bubbles so that Livi can hear what her fans are cheering.

Beautiful Moment

Livi is receiving a Golden Star Award for Best Singer.
What do you think it looks like? Draw the coolest, craziest award
in the space below for Livi to take home!

At the Airport

It's time for check-in. Look carefully at Livi's boarding pass and colour in the star next to the matching barcode.

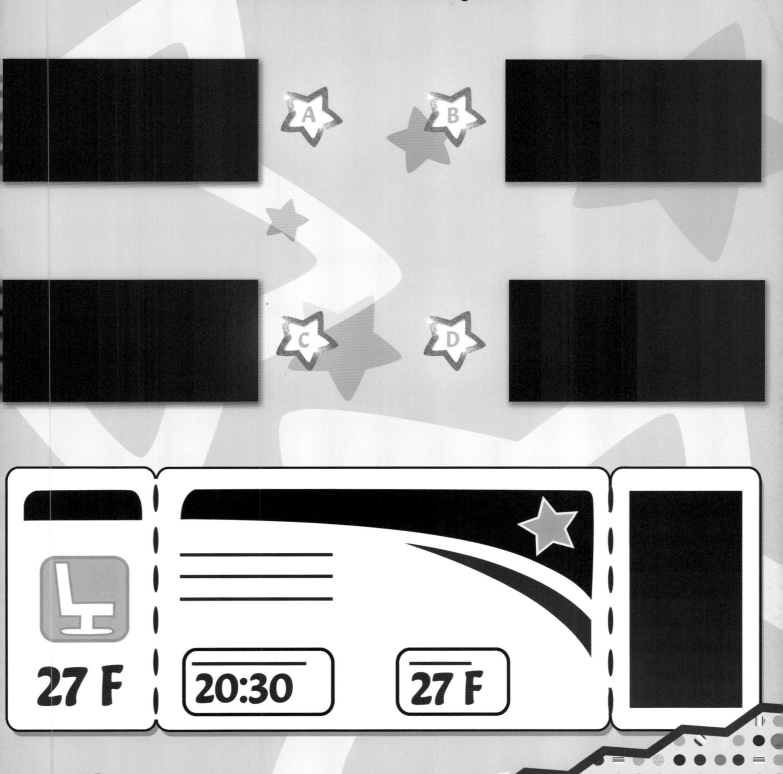

27 F   20:30   27 F

Cartoon Cookie!

What goodbye present would make Livi super happy?
A portrait of her pet Dalmatian, Cookie, of course!
Follow the steps to draw a picture of the adorable puppy.

1.

2.

3.

4.

5.

6.

45

Going Home

It's time for Livi to fly home, but she's promised to return to Heartlake City one day! Look closely to find her among the passengers as she waves goodbye.

Headphone Tangle

Mia loves listening to music! Follow the path of her headphones to find out what she's listening to today.

Studio Spot

The friends are having a tour of Heartlake City's new recording studio!
Join them for a look around. Can you spot which of the small pieces
isn't in the big picture?

1　2　3　4

Magic Mirrors

The funfair's in town, and the friends are enjoying the Hall of Magic Mirrors!
Can you figure out who is in each reflection? Write their name
in the box below each mirror.

Sweet Dreams

Andrea believes that a dreamcatcher can protect you from bad dreams.
So she made one for Emma, to make sure she gets a perfect night's sleep!
Follow these steps to make your own magical dreamcatcher.

You will need:
- a paper plate
- colourful strings and threads
- ribbons
- strips of colourful cloth
- beads
- feathers
- a hole punch
- scissors
- sticky tape

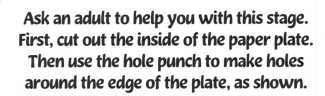

1 Ask an adult to help you with this stage. First, cut out the inside of the paper plate. Then use the hole punch to make holes around the edge of the plate, as shown.

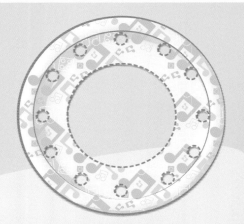

2 Thread a long piece of string through one of the holes and tie a knot at one end. Then tape the knot to the back of the plate to secure it.

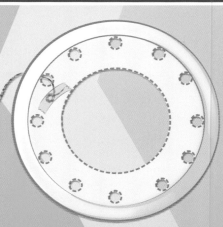

3

Thread the string through the other holes to create a net as shown. When you've finished, tie a knot at the end of the string and stick it to the back of the plate with tape.

4

Decide which is the top and which is the bottom of your dreamcatcher. Tie some ribbons to the bottom, thread on some beads and attach some feathers with sticky tape to decorate it.

5

Tie a loop of string to the top, and now your dreamcatcher is ready to hang up! Sweet dreams!

Answers

pp. 2–3

ANDREA

STEPHANIE

MIA

EMMA

OLIVIA

p. 5

p. 7

p. 9

Mrs Samuels:
Curls – 5:30 p.m.

Mrs Brown:
Colour – 4 p.m.

Noah:
Haircut – 5 p.m.

p. 11

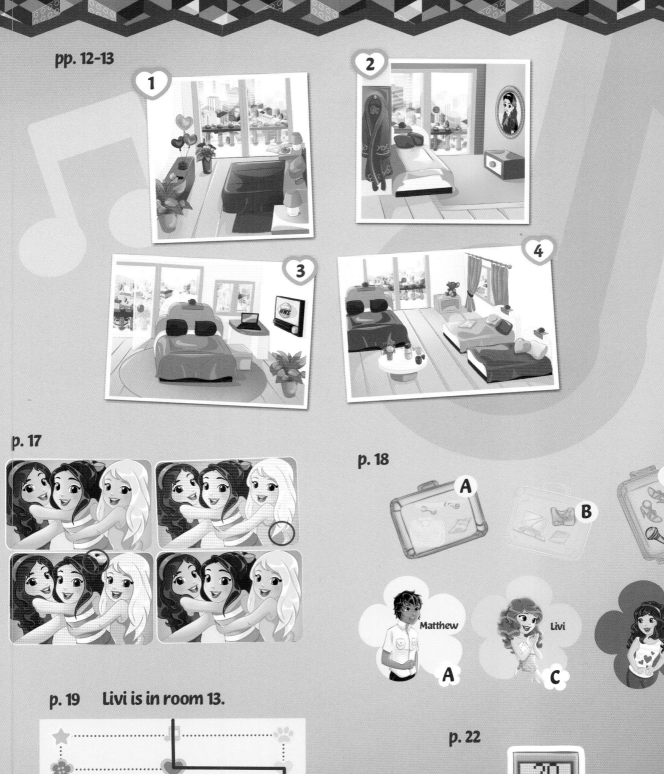

pp. 12–13

p. 17

p. 18

p. 19   Livi is in room 13.

p. 22

Matthew

Livi

Olivia

p. 23

pp. 24–25

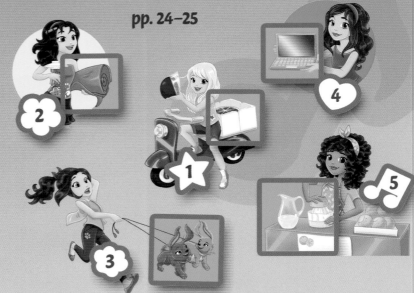

p. 29

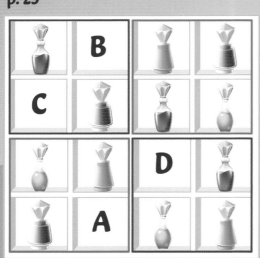

p. 30

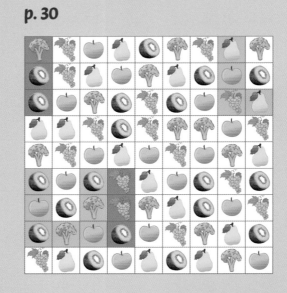

p. 31

B

pp. 32–33

p. 34

p. 35

p. 39

p. 38

C

p. 43

C

pp. 46–47

p. 48

p. 49

2

Wish list:
- ☑ Tulips
- ☐ Water
- ☑ Forest fruit ice cream dessert
- ☑ Exercise mat
- ☐ Bowl for doggie snacks
- ☑ Portrait of Livi's pet

pp. 50–51

STEPHANIE

EMMA

ANDREA

OLIVIA

MIA